CW00665841

CLASSIC LANDF

ANTRIM COAST

CLASSIC LANDFORMS OF THE
ANTRIM COAST

BERNARD SMITH AND PATRICIA WARKE
The Queen's University of Belfast

Series editors
Christopher Green, Michael Naish and Sally Naish

Published by the Geographical Association
in conjunction with the
British Geomorphological Research Group

Geographical
Association

THE BRITISH GEOMORPHOLOGICAL RESEARCH GROUP

PREFACE

Geomorphologists study landforms and the processes that create and modify them. The results of their work, published as they invariably are in specialist journals, usually remain inaccessible to the general public. We should like to put that right. Scattered across the landscapes of England, Wales, Scotland and Ireland there are many beautiful and striking landforms which delight the eye of the general public and are also visited by educational parties from schools, colleges and universities. Our aim in producing this series of guides is to make modern explanations of these classic landforms available to all, in a style and format that will be easy to use in the field. We hope that an informed understanding of the origins of the features will help the visitor to enjoy the landscape all the more.

Encouraged by the success of the first edition of the Classic Landform Guides we are pleased to introduce this new title, enhanced by colour photographs and colour illustrations and with the valuable addition of 1:50,000 map extracts by kind permission of the Ordnance Survey of Northern Ireland. The relevant maps for the area covered in this book are Ordnance Survey of Northern Ireland *Discoverer Series* 1:50,000 sheets 4 (Coleraine), 5 (Ballycastle) and 9 (Ballymena, Larne) and Geological Survey of Northern Ireland sheet 7 of the 1:50,000 *Solid Geology Series* (The Causeway Coast) and 1:250,000 *Solid Geology Series* (Geological Map of Northern Ireland).

Christopher Green *Royal Holloway, University of London*
Michael Naish and Sally Naish *Hayes, Kent*

ISBN 1 899085 47 5
This edition first published 2001
Published by the Geographical Association, 160 Solly Street, Sheffield S1 4BF.
The views expressed in this publication are those of the author and do not necessarily represent those of the Geographical Association.
The Geographical Association is a registered charity no. 313129.
Front cover photograph: Port Noffer with Roveran Valley head and Chimney Tops in the background.
Frontispiece: The Giant's Harp below Chimney Tops.

CONTENTS

Acknowledgements

The author wishes to thank Gill Alexander for preparing the figures and for her tolerance in the face of serial modifications. Also deserving of thanks are numerous colleagues who, through discussion and example, have opened our eyes to the complexities of the Antrim Coast. Prominent among these are Carolynne Ferris, Ross Millar, Julian Orford, John McAlister, Karen Lowther, Ray Bowden, Jill Enderby and Paul Allison. Thanks must also go to David Given for help with aerial photography. Last but not least, special thanks are due to Chris Green for his editorial guidance and forebearance.

Maps reproduced from Ordnance Survey of Northern Ireland 1:50,000 *Discoverer* mapping with the permission of Ordnance Survey of Northern Ireland, Colby House, Stranmillis Court, Belfast BT9 5BG. © Crown Copyright. Permit number: 1062.

Copy Editing: Rose Pipes
Illustrations: Paul Coles
Series design concept: Quarto Design, Huddersfield
Design and typesetting: ATG Design, Catalyst Creative Imaging, Leeds
Printing and binding: Colorcraft Limited, Hong Kong

INTRODUCTION

The north-east corner of Ireland is by any standard a dramatic landscape. It is not surprising therefore that between Larne in the south-east and Portrush in the north-west there are two Areas of Outstanding Natural Beauty (AONBs) and one of only two natural World Heritage Sites in the British Isles – the Giant's Causeway. Although this guide concentrates on features to be found along the often spectacular coastline, the landscape story as a whole is dominated by **basalt** lava flows that form the Antrim Plateau. These are the largest remnants of an ancient volcanic province that once covered north-east Ireland and significant areas of western Scotland.

The basalts formed some 60 million years before present (MYBP), at the beginning of the Tertiary period, flowing out across a complex limestone landscape. They therefore provide a unique opportunity to study landscape conditions and environmental change at the beginning of the Tertiary, when the underlying Cretaceous Chalk had only recently emerged from the sea and the Atlantic Ocean was just beginning to open up. The record of these events is to be found as fossil soils and buried landscapes within the cliffs of the Antrim coastline. In many places, such as at Spy Window (Figure 1), these geological features have been affected by landscape changes that have taken place since the end of the last ice age some 12,000-15,000 years BP (before present). The most obvious of these post-glacial adjustments is recorded as a series of **marine benches** and **raised beach** deposits which reflect the interplay of post-glacial rising sea level and the uplift of the land resulting from isostatic rebound. The most dramatic adjustments are, however, the slope failures that characterise much of the coastline and reflect the response of the landscape as it comes into equilibrium with the post-glacial environment.

The ability to achieve equilibrium depends upon numerous factors, the most significant of which is size or scale. In general, the larger the initial slope failure, the less likely it is to have adjusted to present-day conditions. For example, a major feature of the east Antrim coast is the large **rotational failures**, such as those at Garron Point (Figure 1). The blocks, which are measured in hundreds of metres, are thought to have failed in the immediate post-glacial period when support from Scottish glacial ice in the Irish Sea was removed. These blocks are, however, so large that many thousands of years of weathering and erosion will be required before they will be worn down to form a gentler slope.

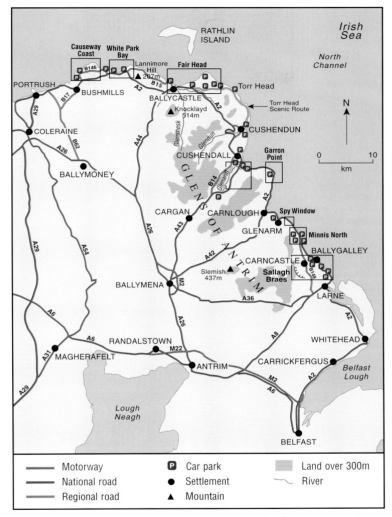

Figure 1: The Antrim Coast: Location and access map showing areas covered in the following chapters.

Superimposed on these major failures are many smaller scale erosional features which modify the larger blocks. The mud flowslides at Minnis North (Figure 1) exemplify this where debris is almost continuously on the move from the front of one of these blocks towards the sea. This process of slope adjustment is promoted by the regular removal of material from the front of the flows by both the action of the sea and human intervention aimed at keeping the coastal road open. Removal of this material maintains the steepness of the slopes and contributes to their continued instability.

The basal removal of material is one of the major controls on cliff shape and is particularly important for the highly unstable north Antrim cliffs such as those along the Causeway Coast. Wherever the coast is sheltered from wave action in the numerous bays, the absence of effective basal removal has allowed either the development of gentler **scree** slopes below basalt cliffs or, as in White Park Bay (Figure 1), a slope of low angled mudflows and slides. On the more exposed headlands, wave attack combined with the efficient removal of fallen debris allows steep cliffs to be maintained. In some instances slope adjustment is more subtle, reflecting differences in composition and structure of successive lava flows, or the presence of beds of weathered basalt that formed on the surface of lava flows in periods between eruptions. These structurally weak beds are best seen at the Giant's Causeway where, unfortunately, they have been excavated to form a cliff path. The resulting combination of rock weakness and artificial over-steepening has inevitably increased instability and highlights the conflict between protecting the coastline and satisfying demands for access by hundreds of thousands of visitors.

The Antrim coast is very complex and there are many pressures upon it. This guide provides an introduction to the area and the issues by highlighting a number of key sites that emphasise the importance of such factors as geological controls, the post-glacial legacy versus the role of present-day slope processes and, more specifically, at the Giant's Causeway, some of the problems of managing access to protected landscapes. Our intention is to bring the picturesque and sometimes dramatic scenery of this part of the UK to a wider audience and to encourage exploration of areas outside the usual tourist route. We do this by taking the reader along a route that begins in the south-east of the region and follows the coast road to the Giant's Causeway (Figure 1). It is important to note, however, that to explore all the sites described the journey may take several days, and it is not essential to follow the route outlined because most of the coastal sites are linked by a network of inland roads that enable the visitor to shorten their trip as desired.

GEOLOGY

The geological framework

The geology of the north-east corner of Ireland can be likened to a rather dilapidated large house. The bulk of the house is built of several floors of Mesozoic sedimentary rocks of Cretaceous, Jurassic and Triassic age (Figure 2). These sit on top of a foundation of older Palaeozoic strata. On top of the house is a thick roof of basalt lava flows put in place at the very beginning of the Tertiary. Since 'construction', the house has been much modified. The most recent decoration is the result of largely superficial erosion and deposition during the last 2 million years when the area was subject to the repeated glacial and interglacial conditions of the Quaternary. The most dramatic changes seem to have occurred during a long period of weathering and erosion during the Tertiary. In this part of Ireland the basalt roof protected underlying sediments from this erosion, but elsewhere in Ireland Mesozoic strata were almost completely removed. This stripping away can be seen in the area between Ballycastle and Cushendun where the geological foundations are exposed (Figure 2). These foundations are seen to be a complicated mixture of rock types of Carboniferous, Devonian and Precambrian age.

Tertiary basalts

Although they are not the oldest rocks in the area, the most important in terms of shaping the present landscape are the Tertiary basalts. They represent by far the largest expanse of volcanic rocks in the British Isles, but were once part of a much larger igneous province which covered much of Northern Ireland and which can still be seen to outcrop on some of the Scottish islands such as Mull. The basalts owe their existence to an outpouring of lava associated with the opening of what is now the North Atlantic Ocean. These eruptions are estimated to have begun between 60 and 62 MYBP and continued intermittently over several million years. Three main phases of volcanic activity are usually identified producing the Lower, Middle and Upper Basalts (Figure 3). Most of the flows appear to have originated from fissures, but there is some evidence of more explosive eruptions. One of the clearest examples of this occurs near the island of Carrickarade on the north Antrim coast (D 062450) (Photo 1, page 12). Here, as you walk down to the famous rope bridge connecting the island to the mainland, it is possible to see in the cliffs layers of banded volcanic ash (tuff) containing volcanic bombs of

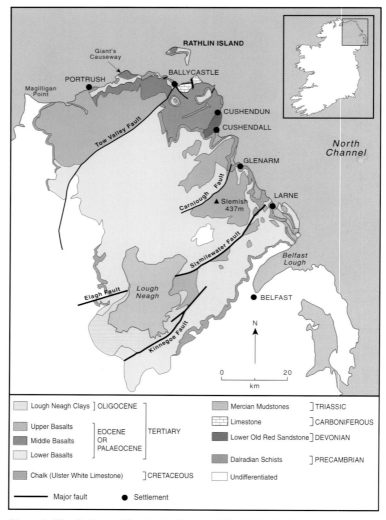

Figure 2: The Geology of the Antrim Plateau, delimited by basalt lavas, and surrounding area.

basalt, Lias clay and limestone. The cliffs on the east of Carrickarade Island are part of a later **dolerite** intrusion while the west side is composed of the basaltic tuff.

Interbasaltic soils

In between the three major phases of basalt extrusion there were two lengthy periods of comparative inactivity (quiescence) during which the lava flows were weathered under humid tropical conditions to form deep soils. In many places this produces a sandwich effect with a thick red filling of weathered interbasaltic soil between two

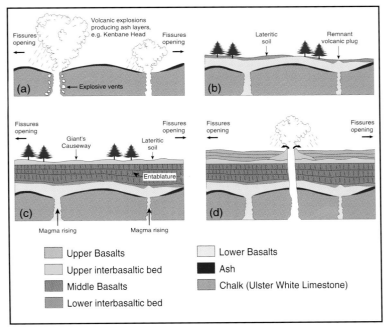

*Figure 3: Stages in the formation of the Antrim basalt group: (a) early Tertiary
rifting and explosive eruptions producing a blanket of ash, (b) outpourings of
Lower Basalt followed by a period of quiescence during which the soils of the lower
interbasaltic bed formed, (c) eruption of the Middle basalts, including the columnar
Causeway basalts followed by soil formation to form the upper interbasaltic bed,
and (d) final phase of volcanic activity laying down the Upper Basalts.
Adapted from: Lyle, 1996.*

layers of basalt. The intense weathering resulted in a relatively rapid
chemical breakdown of the basalt and led to the mobilisation and
removal of the more soluble elements. The soils left behind are,
therefore, dominated by the less mobile constituents such as
aluminium oxide (bauxite) and iron oxides. Like many present-day
tropical soils, differences in local drainage concentrated the iron and
created indurated patches of 'laterite'. These deeply weathered
profiles now form the Upper and Lower interbasaltic beds that crop
out widely across the region and play an important role in controlling
cliff form and stability at sites such as the Giant's Causeway. In
places, the concentration of iron and/or aluminium has been sufficient
to warrant mining and there are numerous disused workings
throughout the Antrim Plateau such as at Cargan (D 174189) south-
west of Glenariff.

Dolerite plugs and sills

Following the final outpourings of lava, the region was subjected to
a phase of explosive volcanic activity in which lavas forced their
way upwards through the layers of basalt to the surface where cinder

Photo 1: Carrickarade: *a complex of banded volcanic ash, basalt and a later dolerite intrusion.*

cones were formed. The loose volcanic debris comprising these cones was quickly eroded to leave the central plugs standing above the present-day land surface. The most prominent of these is Slemish (D 221054), which lies to the east of Ballymena. The lava forming the volcanic plugs is dolerite and elsewhere in the region dolerite also flowed horizontally between basalt flows and the underlying sedimentary strata to form a number of **sills.** The most significant of these sills crops out at Fair Head in the north-east where dramatic vertical cliffs form a natural pivot point between the north and east Antrim coasts.

Cretaceous Chalk

As described at the beginning of this chapter, the basalts of the Antrim Plateau effectively form the roof of a multi-storied accumulation of sedimentary rocks. When the first eruptions occurred, the ash and lava flows covered a complex Cretaceous Chalk landscape. This Chalk (Ulster White Limestone) is harder, denser and better jointed than the Chalk of southern England and because of this is able to support a range of classic **karstic** landforms such as **solution hollows** that can be seen at the edge of the Antrim Plateau infilled with basalt. Like the Chalk of southern England, however, the Antrim Chalk contains beds of flint nodules that, before inundation by the basalt, weathered to produce a residual soil of red (and sometimes grey) clay and flints. This residual soil is preserved as patchy deposits between the Chalk and the overlying basalt, a good example occurring at Spy Window (D 330150) – pages 23-25.

Liassic clays

Beneath the Chalk is the Hibernian Greensand and below that a layer of heavy Liassic clays. These Liassic clays have played a very important role in the shaping of the coastal scenery because of their impermeability and inherent structural weakness. Water that percolates down through the overlying basalt and Chalk has difficulty in percolating through the Liassic clays and tends to saturate the overlying rocks creating conditions of potential instability. In addition, the clays form a structurally weak base for the Chalk and basalt and may either deform or flow out when saturated. Because of these factors, outcrops of the Lias clays tend to be associated with either mud flowslides (e.g. Minnis North – pages 20-23) or with much larger rotational failures in the Chalk and basalt (e.g. Garron Point – pages 26-28). Beneath the Lias clays are Triassic rocks comprising mainly sandstones and mudstones, but these rocks have little surface expression in the area.

The basement, faults and dykes

Below the Triassic beds is the basement of Carboniferous, Devonian and Precambrian rocks which outcrop in the north-east around Fair Head (Figure 1) where the overlying strata have been stripped away (pages 32-34). Although these basement rocks generally form a firm foundation for the rocks of the plateau, there has been subsidence around what is now Lough Neagh. This results in the basalts of the Antrim Plateau dipping gently towards this area, and thus away from the coast – a factor that has accentuated, and helped to maintain the steepness of the coastal cliffs. This subsidence was also associated with reactivation of fault systems in the basement and in many areas dolerite was intruded into these faults creating 'swarms' of **dykes**. These are particularly evident along the Causeway Coast where dolerite dykes run out at right angles from the coastline and are, in part, responsible for the distinctive sequence of bays and headlands (pages 38-49).

Lough Neagh Clays

The only rocks not affected by these faults and dykes are the sediments that washed into the downwarped area during the Middle Tertiary (Oligocene period). These sediments are referred to as the Lough Neagh Clays, but in reality they comprise a mixture of clays, sands and silts and, most significantly, extensive deposits of **lignite** up to 350m in thickness.

SEA-LEVEL CHANGE AND COASTAL CONTROLS

Sea-level change

Sea-level change has been the primary control on development of the Antrim coastline since the disappearance of glacial ice. During the Pleistocene, Northern Ireland was subject to repeated glaciations. The most recent and most influential with regard to coastal development was the last glacial episode which extended from approximately 30,000 to 17,000 years BP. During this time large quantities of glacial and marine sediments were transported and deposited on and around the coast. In addition to the deposition of sediment, the land mass experienced significant isostatic subsidence (c. 150-200m) due to the weight of ice. Following ice retreat, the interaction between isostatic rebound of the land and sea-level readjustment created a complex pattern of sea-level change (Carter, 1982, 1991) (Figure 4 and Table 1).

The most obvious features attesting to past sea-level change are late- and post-glacial marine terraces and raised beach deposits, which can be traced around much of the Antrim coast. In particular, the A2 coast road north of Larne follows a series of raised beaches several metres above present-day high water mark and backed by former sea cliffs.

Irrefutable evidence of past sea-level change exists around the Antrim coast although many difficulties arise when trying to tie down precisely the sequence of change because of the complex interplay of isostatic rebound and sea-level readjustment. Although **isostasy** is now of less significance, the dynamic character of the coastline will continue, particularly if the impact of global warming on sea level assumes a greater significance as a control on future coastal modification.

Coastal controls

The Antrim coast comprises a variety of landforms including rock and earth cliffs, rock platforms, sandy beaches and gravel or boulder beaches. Much of the large-scale configuration of the coastline in this region is controlled by an assemblage of faults and volcanic intrusions. White Park Bay, for example, is bounded by geological faults while the dramatic basalt cliffs of the Causeway Coast reflect the structural controls exerted by the combination of several basalt flows and interbasaltic beds.

In addition to structural and geological factors, the coastline has been shaped over time by constant attack from the sea. The erosive force of the sea involves the combined action of two types of waves

Table 1: Approximate time spans for major events in the development of the Antrim coast.

Era	Post-glacial	
Holocene	Future ?	Global forecast of sea-level rise and increased storminess may lead to eventual widespread reworking and/or destruction of sand and gravel landforms.
	Present- c. 2000 years BP	Only minor changes in sea level due to the final phase of isostatic readjustment. This prolonged period of relative sea-level stability has contributed to current beach sediment shortage as sediments are worked out and not replaced.
	c. 2000-5000 years BP	Sea level fell by a few metres as isostatic rebound of the landmass continued, leaving a narrow raised beach along much of the coast.
	c. 5000-10,000 years BP	Sea level rose rapidly as ice melt refilled the oceans and ultimately reached some 2-3m above the present-day level forming transgressive dune sequences and gravel ridges by moving onshore glacio-marine sediment deposited during the late glacial period when sea level was high.
	c. 13,000 years BP	As the ice retreated and the land rebounded, sea level initially fell quite rapidly to possibly some 30-40m below its present level. It is suggested that at this time Ireland and Scotland may have had a land link (Devoy, 1985).
Pleistocene	Late glacial	
	c. 18,000 years BP	Towards the end of the last ice age, sea level was more than 20m above present-day level primarily because the land was depressed by the weight of ice. Large amounts of glacio-marine sediments were deposited at this time creating late-glacial marine terraces.
	Earlier Pleistocene	
	c. 2 MYBP	Alternating glacial and interglacial episodes.
Tertiary	c. 2-65 MYBP	Outpouring of basaltic lavas, intrusion of dolerite dykes and sills. Stripping away of Mesozoic rocks in areas unprotected by the basalts. Deposition of Lough Neagh Clays.
Mesozoic Era	c. 65-180 MYBP	Deposition of Triassic sandstones, Hibernian Greensand and Chalk.
Palaeozoic Era	c. 180-365 MYBP	Deposition of Precambrian, Carboniferous and Devonian rocks.

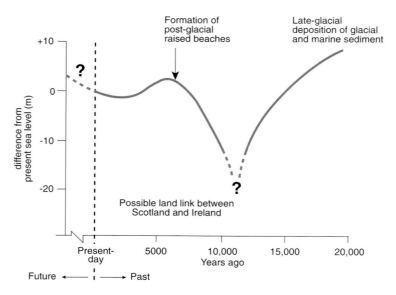

Figure 4: Composite sea-level change curve *for the east and north coasts of County Antrim. After: Carter, 1991.*

– swell and sea waves. Much of the north Antrim coast is dominated by swell waves. Swell waves are several hundreds of metres in wavelength and are the product of major storms having their origins far out in the Atlantic Ocean. They often travel thousands of kilometres before reaching land and can build up to a height of several metres as water depth decreases on the approach to land where they generally break parallel to the shore to form surf. Because of the dominance of swell waves, the north Antrim coast is a region of relatively high wave energy with an average wave height greater than 50cm, but the impact of Atlantic swell diminishes in importance in Irish Sea waters off the east Antrim coast.

Although swell waves penetrate well into the Irish Sea, the east Antrim coast is dominated by the smaller surface-wind generated sea waves, which create moderate wave energy conditions with average wave heights of 20-50cm. Sea waves tend to approach the shoreline at an angle, creating a longshore current. Despite the existence of a relatively strong southerly longshore drift component along the east Antrim coast, it has a minor impact on present-day sediment supply because of the dearth of available sediment entering the system.

There are several reasons for the limited sediment availability around the Antrim coast. As noted above, the most significant influx of sediment occurred towards the end of the last ice age. This sediment comprised a mix of glacially transported debris and marine sands. Some of it formed the sand and gravel features now preserved as raised beaches, while during the comparatively consistent sea-level conditions of the last 2000 years much of the remaining sediment has

16

Photo 2: Coastal defences near Minnis North. *The sea wall tends to reflect wave energy and leads to erosion of beach sediments with removal of fine material leaving boulder beaches, as can be seen in the foreground.*

been locked into inactive coastal sediment accumulations or lost offshore. Inputs of riverine sediments have also declined because of human-made modifications of river channels. Some sediment continues to be eroded directly from the basalt and chalk cliffs but this tends to form gravel and boulder deposits that are not readily broken down or transported except during extreme storm events. Moreover, in many locations along the east Antrim coast road defensive sea walls have been constructed and these have greatly reduced the amount of fresh sediment entering the near-shore system and have, by creating a reflective barrier, led to the erosion of existing beach deposits (Photo 2).

SLOPE INSTABILITY

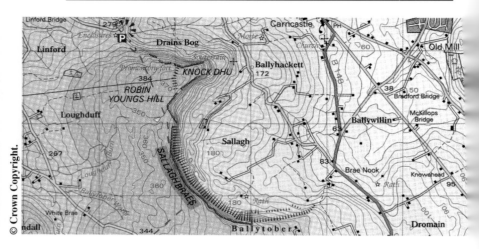

Sallagh Braes

Leaving Larne on the main coast road (A2) travelling north brings you to the small town of Ballygalley (D 3707) which is located in front of the toe of a mass of slumped material. This material emanates from a large rotational feature some 4.5km to the south-west called Sallagh Braes. Because of its size, this feature is particularly evident on the Ordnance Survey of Northern Ireland 1:50,000 map. The corrie-like backwall and bowl can be viewed more closely by leaving the A2 coast road at Ballygalley and heading west to Carncastle and then south along the B148 to Brae Nook (D 361054). At the Brae Nook road junction a minor road turns north-west across the bowl of Sallagh Braes. The irregular hummocky terrain comprises debris from the original large-scale failure that is still active in places, and at points along the road the carriageway has been deflected downslope, with small lobes of slumped material visible in several of the fields on the right below the road.

The bowl at Sallagh Braes is approximately 2km in diameter and thus comprises the largest rotational feature to be found along the Antrim coast. It is suggested that if ice streamed parallel to the coast and undercut the plateau edge after removing superficial deposits, unstable and unsupported slopes would have been exposed once the ice receded. The combination of these unstable slopes and underlying clay-rich Liassic beds would have encouraged slope failure, especially in the immediate post-glacial period when the land was 'relaxing' as ice loading decreased and abundant water was available to act as an aid to slippage. During this post-glacial period of readjustment many major failures occurred, as demonstrated at Sallagh Braes where jointed basalt and chalk slumped and moved downslope towards the coast. Sallagh Braes is now largely a relict feature, inactive under present-day conditions, but a significant illustration of the inherent instability of the Antrim coast.

Minnis North

Rejoining the A2 and heading north from Ballygalley brings you to a section of coastline which exhibits extensive evidence of contemporary instability, albeit at a much smaller scale than that at Sallagh Braes. This entire coastline is dominated by an integrated system of landslides and other slope failures operating at a range of scales. In detail it can be seen that small terraces or 'terracettes' cut across many of the low angled slopes. These are generally taken to indicate the downward **creep** of the superficial glacial **till** that covers many of the lower slopes and/or the Lias clays that underlie it. When viewed from afar, however, it can be seen that what appears to be the cliff line is only the front of a series of large, rotated landslides that extend up to half a kilometre inland before the true edge of the plateau is reached. Typically, each landslide consists of an arcuate block of basalt above chalk that has both dropped and rotated backwards. This forms a steep cliff behind the block, a backwards-tilted surface that was formerly part of the plateau and a forward edge to the block that was once the cliff edge (Figure 5). Because of the contrast between the black basalt and white chalk, these rotated blocks are clearly visible as you drive along the coast road. The origin of these failures lies not, however, in the chalk and basalt. Instead, the controlling factors are the structurally weak Lias clays beneath them, combined with the over-steepening of the coast during the last glaciation and the disappearance of supporting Irish Sea ice. The resulting failures both pushed back the plateau edge and elevated the Lias to form much of the coastline.

The most obvious location where the Lias has been exposed at the coast is at Minnis North, visible just after the junction of the B148 and A2 (at D 347124). Minnis North (D 340136) is the name given by a succession of geomorphologists to one of the most intensively studied slope failure complexes in the whole of the British Isles. Essentially it is a flowslide system contained within the front slope of a rotated landslide. They are termed flowslides because elements of both flow and slide occur during failure episodes. The lateral extent of the flowslide is very limited (Figure 6) and belies the intensity with which it was monitored throughout the 1970s (e.g. Prior *et al.*, 1971; Davies and Stephens, 1978). They identified two linked elements to the system. The first of these is an upper basin or bowl in which debris accumulates from surrounding slopes and the chalk escarpment behind it. This material feeds into the lower section (or toe) of the system that comprises a series of clearly defined channels in which

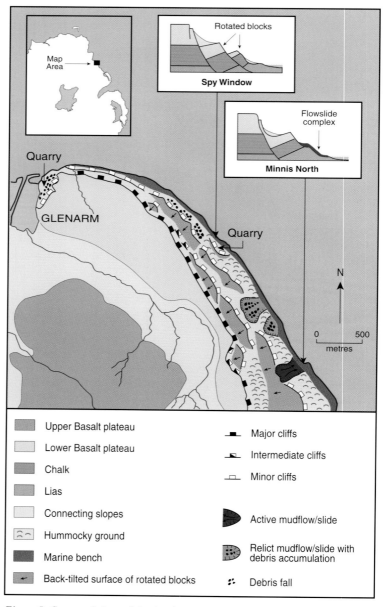

Figure 5: Geomorphology of the Antrim coast south of Glenarm, showing multiple rotated blocks in front of the plateau margin. Schematic sections show the generalised structure of these slope failures at Minnis North and Spy Window quarry.

mixtures of glacial till, Lias clays, chalk and basalt debris periodically flow downslope. Movement begins as a fast moving flow, but as water drains away it slows down to a slide at the slope foot (Figure 7a). The

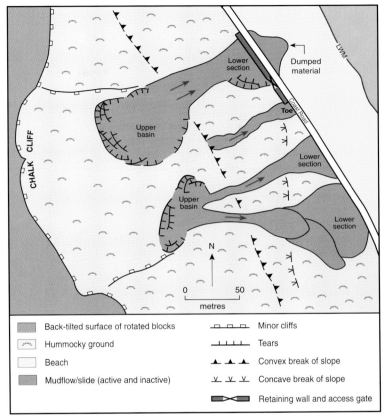

Figure 6: The main elements of the flowslide complex at Minnis North. Adapted from: Prior et al., 1971.

trigger for the flows appears to be prolonged rainfall that saturates the slope, followed by a period of intense rainfall that generates a 'positive pore water pressure'. This is when so much water enters the slope that it begins to force individual soil and rock particles apart and these materials begin to take on the properties of a liquid. At this point water flows out onto the hillslope and ponds on the surface. Soon afterwards, material starts to flow downslope in channels defined by sharp 'shear planes' or failure surfaces with characteristic striations scratched by debris in the passing flow.

Historically, this material would then have flowed out onto the marine bench in front of the cliff and blocked the coast road. In more recent years, a retaining wall has been built across the base of the most active feeder channel (Figure 7b and Photo 3). Debris is regularly removed from behind the wall and dumped offshore. The effect of this is to create a buffer zone that can absorb most flows, but the constant steepening of the toe slope may, ironically, increase slope instability. Although rainfall is the key to triggering the flowslides, the

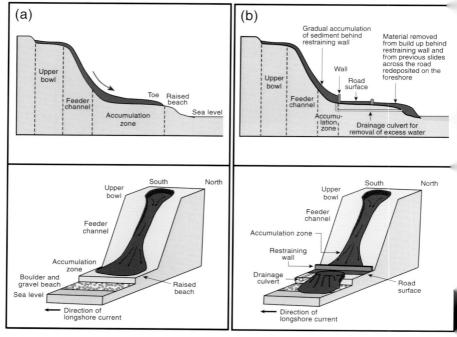

Figure 7: The structure of the flowside complex at Minnis North: (a) before and (b) after construction of the retaining wall. Construction of the Antrim coast road in the mid-1800s contributed to slope instability through regular removal of material from the toe and maintenance of an oversteepened slope.

Photo 3: The most active of the feeder channels, showing the buffer zone behind the retaining wall, the culvert below the road that allows drainage of excess water, and the toe of dumped material on the far side of the coast road. Photo: Alan Robertson.

precise relationships are unclear, and similar rainfall patterns may or may not lead to a flow depending upon the nature of previous rainfall and the history of recent flows. This makes prediction very difficult and uncertainty is increased by the presence of numerous potential channels, any one of which could be the site of the next flow. Although Minnis North is particularly active, there are several other former flowslides along the coast road characterised by low-angled debris slopes. In general, the outcome of these failures is the reduction of the former sea cliff into a gentler equilibrium slope. The complexity of the present-day landscape suggests that this is a very slow process with a considerable way to go.

Spy Window

The quarry at Spy Window (also known as Madman's Window) is located on the landward side of the A2 coast road at D 330150 approximately 2km north of the Minnis mudflows. Like Minnis North, Spy Window is not cut into the edge of the Antrim Plateau but was created by the quarrying of chalk from the front of the large rotated blocks that characterise this part of the coastline (Figure 5 and Photo 4). There is now a car park and picnic area on the seaward side of the road together with an information board that briefly describes the geology of the site. From this vantage point the relationship between the chalk and overlying basalt is evident. Also evident within the chalk are lines of flint that have made excavation and crushing an expensive process. It is not the nature of the two geological units that is of greatest interest at this site, but the characteristics of the boundary between them. This boundary provides an ideal opportunity

Photo 4: Spy Window, *left of centre by the coast road, and the series of rotational failures that make up the coastal zone in front of the main plateau escarpment. See Figure 5, page 19.*

to study the chalk landscape that was covered by the first of the Tertiary lava flows.

The surface of the chalk landscape was not regular, but was pockmarked by numerous deep and steep-sided solution hollows leading down into a dense network of solution-widened joints. These hollows were infilled by dark red iron-rich clays containing flints (Photo 5). The clays have a similar iron-rich composition and blocky structure to present-day **terra rossa** soils in the Mediterranean Basin. It is dangerous to automatically assume that the region must have been subject to a Mediterranean type of climate. Global climatic conditions at the beginning of the Tertiary were very different and it may be that there were warm, moist climatic types that have no present-day equivalent. The solution hollows were not always filled with clays and flints, as close examination shows both surface solutional etching of the chalk and bedding within the infill suggesting that the material was progressively washed into the hollows. Descriptions from other quarries have identified lignite layers and large sections of fossilised tree trunks in the infill indicating that the surrounding landscape must have had extensive soil and vegetation cover. On the basis of this evidence it is suggested that the vegetation cover was destroyed or at least burnt back during the early phase of basalt eruptions. Without the protective vegetation cover, the soil could have been washed into low-lying areas and recent research has tentatively identified volcanic ash deposits within infill material.

Photo 5: The quarry face at Spy Window: *former solution hollows on the chalk landscape, infilled by red clays and flints and overlain by the Lower Basalts.*

24

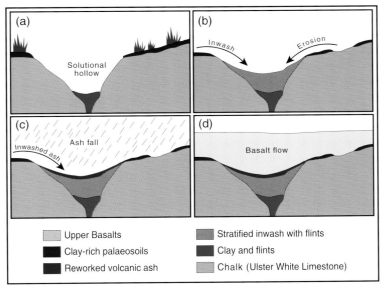

Figure 8: Possible environmental changes associated with the onset of volcanic activity in the early Tertiary: (a) chalk landscape with solution hollows and thin soil cover, (b) soil degradation, erosion and inwash into solution hollows possibly associated with destruction of vegetation, (c) ashfall and washing of ash into hollows, and (d) capping of landscape by Lower Basalts, baking the top layers of chalk and infills.

As the eruptions continued, the chalk landscape would have been buried beneath the basalt, which partially baked the top of the chalk and the upper layers of clay infills where the lavas flowed into the former solution hollows. This sequence of events is illustrated diagrammatically in Figure 8.

The value of the features at Spy Window quarry and at other sites around the coast is that they provide a unique insight into the environmental conditions prior to and on the margins of a major volcanic eruption. They can also be used to deduce information about climatic conditions at this formative time in Earth history. Similar 'clay with flints' deposits are found in the chalk uplands of southern England and northern France but because they sit on top of the chalk it is difficult to date them and to rule out reworking by other weathering and erosion processes. The great advantage of the Antrim sub-basaltic beds is that they can be dated precisely because of their burial with no opportunity for reworking of infill material. The structures that we see are, therefore, those that formed during a period of intense landscape change some 60 MYBP.

GARRON POINT

Photo 6: Rotational failures in the chalk and basalt at Garron Point.

The theme of slope instability is continued at Garron Point (D 303242), a site reached by continuing north along the A2 through the villages of Glenarm and Carnlough (Figure 1). At this site the relationship between the Cretaceous chalk and overlying Tertiary basalt is clearly shown with both strata dipping towards the south-west (Photo 6).

Garron Point comprises a major rockfall complex that extends for approximately 1 to 1.5km around the Point (Photo 7). The large rotational rock slides at this site form a major feature of the Antrim coast with many of the larger blocks more than 100m across. These rotational features are thought to have been most active in the immediate post-glacial period, as at Sallagh Braes. When the supporting ice had gone the land was no longer loaded with ice and abundant moisture was available to aid slippage.

As at Minnis North, the large-scale rotational failures may effectively be viewed as relict features under present-day conditions and surface modification of the slopes continues through smaller-scale rockfalls, debris slides and dissection of the larger blocks.

Photo 7: Garron Point: *multiple rotational failures, collapses within the basalt escarpment and an artificial causeway built to allow construction of the coast road.*

However, present-day modification is not restricted to slope failure but also includes weathering of the basalt and chalk. An excellent example of modification through weathering can be seen at a site just before the A2 road reaches Garron Point where a small car park on the seaward side of the road provides access to a chalk promontory with coastal karst development (D 303237).

At this site the chalk is directly exposed to marine action with the result that several weathering zones can be identified related to their proximity to the sea and the weathering forms that are typical of so-called **marine karst**. The intertidal and splash zones are most directly affected by marine activity and are characterised by extensive pitting of the chalk surface attributed to **salt weathering** and limited biological weathering by lichen and algae. Analysis of surface samples has identified a hierarchy of pitting with pits 10μm in diameter in the base of pits several millimetres in diameter which in turn lie within pits some 1-2cm wide. Further back from the wave-dominated zones are the spray and landward zones, which are characterised by different weathering forms comprising larger-scale solution pans and solution-widened joints (Photos 8a and 8b). With increasing distance from the direct influence of the sea the importance of salt weathering decreases while that of chemical dissolution increases.

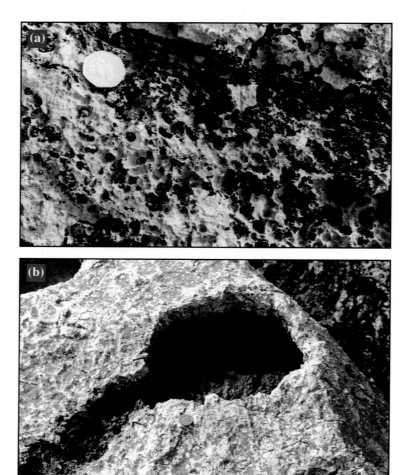

Photo 8: Marine karst on the shore platform at Garron Point: *(a) pitting in the splash zone attributed to the combination of biological and salt weathering mechanisms, and (b) solution pan in the spray zone with overflow channel.*

GLENARIFF

The nine Glens of Antrim dissect the Antrim Plateau all along its eastern side providing natural settlement locations where the broad valleys reach the sea (Figure 1). They also provide agricultural land in an otherwise bleak upland area with no coastal plains.

The Antrim Glens trend north-east to south-west and are associated with the westward extension of the Highland Boundary Fault Zone in Scotland. The largest and most dramatic of the glens is Glenariff (Photo 9) which is reached by following the A2 coastal road west of Garron Point. The sides of Glenariff drop steeply from the edge of the Antrim Plateau at *c*. 300m to a broad flat-floored valley. Over these steep upper slopes numerous streams which rise on the plateau plunge into the valley (Photo 10). The great breadth of Glenariff is attributed to the influence of faults that have facilitated downcutting by the Glenariff river through basalt plateau rock and the subsequent removal of this material during glacial episodes.

On the north of Red Bay at Waterfoot (D 240252), the Glenariff River enters the sea through a series of low dunes fronted by a sandy beach. The beach extends along the entire foreshore of Red Bay but removal of sand and gravel over time for agricultural purposes has destroyed a dune system that used to lie at the centre of the bay. Although no long-term trend has been identified, Carter (1991) used photographic records to indicate that the whole shoreline is showing signs of erosion. The cliffs along the northern shore from Waterfoot show evidence of a time when sea level was higher than at present in the form of caves and raised beaches.

Photo 9: Glenariff.

Inland from Waterfoot, the slopes and floor of Glenariff Valley bear witness to its value as agricultural land and the relationship between land use and topography. Glenariff contains good examples of striped or 'ladder farms' with the stone wall field boundaries still clearly showing the division of land. Each smallholder had use of a variety of land types extending from marshy meadows on the valley floor through better drained arable land on the lower slopes to the steep rocky grazing pastures on the upper valley slopes. As with all the other Antrim Glens, the intensity of farming was much greater in the past – a fact borne out by abandoned farm dwellings and neglected stone walls.

Iron ore was once shipped to England from Red Bay from the mid-1800s to the early-1900s. A now dismantled railway ran the length of Glenariff Valley on its southern slopes and transported iron ore mined from interbasaltic exposures on the plateau. Bauxite was also mined from these exposures. One such mine (now disused) is Cargan (D 174189), which lies south-west of Glenariff beside the A43 just before the village of Cargan. Laboratory analysis of samples from a cutting at this site shows the material to comprise more than 30% iron oxide and between 30 and 40% aluminium oxide. These interbasaltic exposures bear witness to the tropical conditions that prevailed during the Tertiary when the basalts of the Antrim Plateau were being erupted.

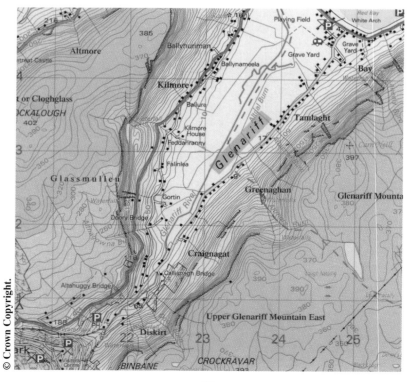

Photo 10: One of many waterfalls draining off the Antrim plateau over the basalt escarpment into Glenariff.

In addition to their scenic and agricultural value, the Antrim Glens provide natural lines of communication between coastal and inland settlements. However, it is important to remember that these features owe their existence to large-scale regional faulting and reflect the action of significant tectonic forces.

FAIR HEAD

North of Glenariff, the A2 passes several of the other Antrim Glens. Before reaching the village of Cushendun there is a choice of route – either continue on the A2 directly to Ballycastle or join the B92 at Mullarts (approximately 4km north of Cushendall) (D 228309). Drive through Cushendun and then follow the signposts for the Torr Head Scenic Route. This follows the coastline north to Torr Head and then turns inland over the plateau surface formed by the Fair Head sill (see Figure 1).

Fair Head is one of the most striking features in the Tertiary igneous rocks of the Antrim coast. Fair Head (also referred to as Benmore Head) is a sill mainly composed of dolerite which was intruded horizontally during the Tertiary into gently dipping lower Carboniferous limestones (Figure 9). Erosion of the overlying limestone beds has left the sill as a dramatic promontory (Photo 11). Vertical jointing of the dolerite forms impressive columnar structures that emphasise the sheerness of the cliff face. The cliffs at Fair Head rise approximately 120m above sea level and are fronted by an apron of talus slopes comprising accumulated debris from toppled and fractured columns. The talus or block scree which surrounds the foot of Fair Head is thought to be primarily of late- and post-glacial age because Scottish ice advancing across the North Channel of the Irish Sea would almost certainly have removed any pre-glacial debris.

Fair Head is best described as a coastal 'pivot point' marking the boundary between the Atlantic Ocean and the Irish Sea as well as a change in coastal form from a north to south to an east to west orientation. Although Fair Head is best viewed from Ballycastle, where it forms a dramatic backdrop, its control on the overlying landscape is evident all along the Torr Head Scenic Route over the plateau. The surface

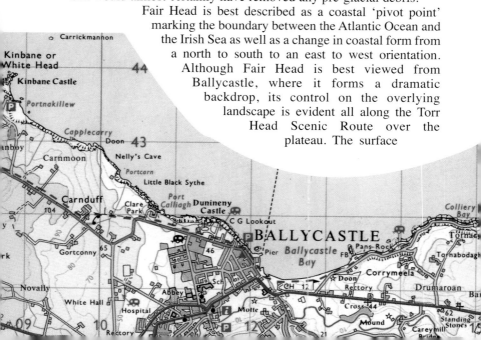

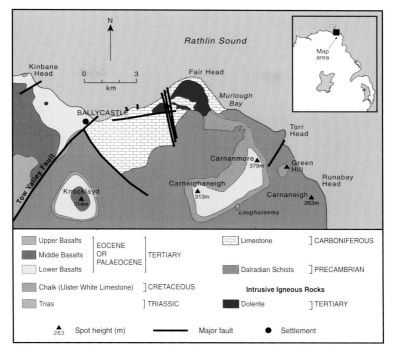

Figure 9: The geology of the area behind Fair Head: this shows the location of basement rocks with basalt and chalk outliers at the Knocklayd, Carneighaneigh, Carnanmore and the dolerite sill at Fair Head.

Photo 11: The Fair Head dolerite still with an apron of scree. The glaciated surface above the sill supports a number of shallow lakes including Lough na Cranagh which contains an artificial island or 'crannog'.

of the Fair Head sill shows evidence of glacial erosion in the form of roches moutonnées and glacial striae. Both of these features occur around Lough na Cranagh with striae trending north-north-east. The somewhat bleak heather covered plateau is strewn with lakes, the largest of which, Lough na Cranagh (D 1742), contains a reasonably well-preserved crannog in its centre. Crannogs are artificial islands constructed from a variety of materials and were defensive structures. When they were first constructed is disputed but there is evidence to suggest that island habitation had already started by the Neolithic. There is no doubt, however, that a settlement atop the Fair Head sill would have provided a dramatic, if somewhat exposed, defensive location.

At the foot of the Antrim Plateau west of Fair Head lies the coastal town of Ballycastle, which has grown around the confluence of the Tow, Glenshesk and Carey rivers. The town has experienced several major floods in the last two decades and particularly in 1990. The floods have been attributed to the combined effects of periods of intense precipitation, short, steep river catchments and wet antecedent conditions resulting in saturated upper catchments. Rainfall is therefore collected from a large upland catchment and then funnelled down narrow valleys to the coast through Ballycastle. In addition to these factors, recent changes in the hydrological characteristics of the rivers have also been identified as major contributory factors. The changes are manifest in a move to a '**flashier**' flow regime where the lag time between the onset of precipitation and peak river discharge is greatly reduced. This alteration could be related to land use change in the upper catchments where increased artificial drainage needed for mechanical peat extraction and afforestation has reduced the storage capacity of peat cover on the Antrim Plateau.

WHITE PARK BAY

Access and safety

To reach White Park Bay take the B15 out of Ballycastle past the Marine Hotel and head west along the north Antrim coast in the direction of Ballintoy. Approximately 3.5km west of Ballintoy, a minor road runs down to a car park and youth hostel at White Park Bay (D 014436). The Bay is accessible on foot from the car park via a path and some steps. White Park Bay has been owned and managed by the National Trust since 1938 and was designated as an Area of Special Scientific Interest (ASSI) in 1996. Over the years the National Trust management strategy has helped minimise tourist impact on the site and has ensured its relatively unspoilt character. **It is important to note that although the waters of White Park Bay may appear to be extremely inviting, especially during summer months, there are rip currents between the sand bars that make the beach a very dangerous place for swimming.**

White Park Bay experiences high wave energy as a result of its position on the swell-wave dominated north Antrim coast but it has a low tidal range. It is a classic embayment bounded by faults – the east to west trending Portbraddan Fault and the north to south trending Lemnagh Fault (Figure 10). All along the Antrim coastline the Tertiary basalts, Cretaceous Chalk and underlying Liassic clays appear at different levels relative to each other because of the effect of faulting. This is evident at the western end of White Park Bay where the basalt of Gid Point (D 0044) has been brought down to sea level by movement along the Portbraddan Fault, setting it side by side with the older Cretaceous Chalk. In addition to the effects of faulting, the landforms within White Park Bay owe much to other geological factors. Wind-blown sand overlies a landslip complex composed of Cretaceous Chalk which has collapsed from the back cliffs onto underlying lubricated Lias clays occasionally exposed among beach sands and dunes. The preferential movement of water above the Lias beds, which has percolated down through the chalk, is made evident by a springline that marks the junction between Lias clays and Cretaceous Chalk. As we have seen at sites such as Minnis North on the east Antrim coast these clays provide an extremely unstable layer over which blocks of chalk readily move in the presence of high pore water pressures.

The dune system is composed of sands that are said to 'sing' as they are walked on because of the well-rounded character of the grains. The dune system is somewhat deceptive because it comprises only a relatively thin veneer of sand overlying the numerous landslips that

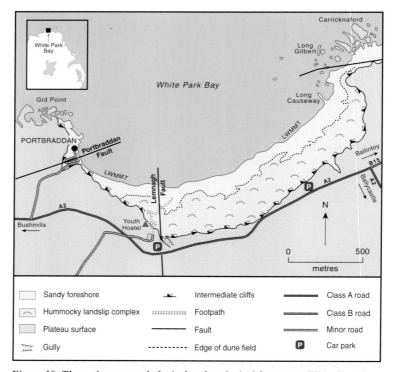

Figure 10: The main geomorphological and geological features at White Park Bay.

form the back slope at the foot of the chalk cliff, creating a transition zone between the cliff and the beach (Photo 12). The irregularity of the surface has facilitated the development of a complex mix of pockets of wet and dry soils in which a rich assemblage of both bog and dune plants may be found such as meadow cranesbill, pyramidal orchids and wild thyme. Regular sheep and cattle grazing help to restrict invasive species and maintain this habitat diversity.

In the shallow offshore waters there is a double series of transitional crescentric sandbars. These are highly dynamic near-shore features that are often reworked and moved closer to or along the shoreline during storm events. Although not visible from the land, the significance of the sandbars lies in their influence on localised coastal stability, primarily because they act as sediment stores and help to dissipate and redirect wave energy. Changes in the position of the sandbars are usually matched by changes in the beach profile. Consequently, when sand is being redistributed along the shore there may be some localised short-term erosion of the beach. Over the long-term, however, the beach at White Park Bay is reasonably stable.

Despite conditions of relative stability within the context of prevailing coastal processes, White Park Bay is under threat due to sand and gravel extraction for agricultural purposes. Until recent decades removal of sediment by local farmers did not pose a serious

Photo 12: White Park Bay looking east: showing the thin cover of vegetated dunes on top of hummocky ground formed by multiple landslips.

problem, primarily because non-mechanical methods of extraction were used, thereby limiting the extent of damage. However, in recent years the use of mechanised diggers has increased the quantity and frequency of removal with an associated long-term increase in threat to this fragile and biologically diverse site. Sand and gravel extraction continues because those who practice it regard it as an historical right enshrined in common law. Through the provision of alternative sources of sand and gravel the National Trust hopes to limit future damage to the site.

During the latter stages of the last glaciation the pressure of the ice sheet against the Antrim coast affected the normal drainage pattern by blocking coastal outlets. Consequently, there was a redirection of drainage all around the coastline with waters that would normally have drained eastwards into the Irish Sea moved westwards through temporary spillways. The most important of these channels is the Loughareema (vanishing lake) Channel which crosses the col between Glendun and the Carey River valley (D 209350 to D 202362). Along the north coast, local and probably short-lived lakes existed in most of the coastal embayments and north-facing valleys during the melting of the ice and many of these may have drained south over what is now high ground. For example, at White Park Bay meltwater may have drained south through a valley west of Lannimore Hill (D 043433) in which drainage now flows north into the bay. Another example of a major spillway occurs inland from the Giant's Causeway and runs for a distance of approximately 4km between Lisnagunogue (D 976428) and Causeway Head (D 945438). This channel now only carries a small stream but, for a short time at the end of the last ice age, must have carried an enormous volume of meltwater.

From White Park Bay one or two routes can be taken to the Giant's Causeway – the less scenic A2, or the B146 which follows a section of the coastline past Dunseverick Castle (D 987446). Dunseverick Castle was a stronghold in the Dark Age kingdom of Dalriada which united north-east Ulster and south-west Scotland. The Castle was eventually wrecked by Cromwellian troops and is little more than a ruin now.

THE GIANT'S CAUSEWAY

Access

The arrival point for most visitors to the Causeway Coast is the Visitors' Centre from where they are whisked to the Giant's Causeway by minibus, thus missing good views of this striking coastline. The best way to view the Causeway Coast is to walk westwards along the cliff top path from the ruins of Dunseverick Castle (D 987446), over Benbane Head for approximately 6km to the Visitors' Centre at the Causeway (D 945439). Even if you do not have the time for this walk, there are several shorter walks closer to the Visitors' Centre that offer the chance to view important sections of the coast. For example, the cliff top path east from the Visitors' Centre provides excellent views of the coastline in both directions and a view of the Causeway itself from above. After a short walk along the cliff-top path it is possible to descend to the foreshore and the Causeway via the Shepherd's Path. If you have the time it is well worth walking a little further north to Roveran Valley Head for excellent views of the coast and the Causeway in profile (see front cover). Below the headland, one can look into the steep embayment of The Amphitheatre (D 9545) to see fine examples of columnar basalt and some of the most active screes and debris falls along the coastline.

From the headland it is also possible to see what remains of the old lower footpath that ran eastwards along the coast almost halfway up the cliffs. Its closure in 1994 was triggered by a series of major landslides that swept away sections of the path which now finishes at a gate below Roveran Valley Head. The remaining section of the path does allow inspection of basalt columns at The Organ, of the interbasaltic bed before the gate, and of one of the numerous dolerite dykes at the gate itself.

Background

There are two common misconceptions concerning the Causeway Coast. The first is that the only area of interest is that immediately around the Giant's Causeway itself, when in fact there are many kilometres of spectacular coastline to the east and west of it. The second is the view that the Causeway was formed some 60 MYBP by volcanic activity. Although the building blocks of the Causeway did form this long ago, and continue to exert a major influence on the landscape, the detailed features we see today are much younger. Indeed, it is only as recently as 15,000 years BP that the coastline emerged from beneath a cover of ice. Since this time, a series of landscape adjustments has not only produced the three small promontories that comprise the Giant's Causeway, but also a number of steep-sided headlands and deep bays fringed by vegetated screes below basalt cliffs. These adjustments have consisted of interactions between a complex geology and marine erosion along an exposed Atlantic shoreline to produce a wide array of active and relict slope failures.

Geological controls

The geological sequence at the Causeway Coast is most clearly seen along the many headlands and is described in detail in an excellent book by Paul Lyle (1996). Typically it consists of a clearly visible red interbasaltic bed sandwiched between the Lower and Middle basalts, each made up of multiple lava flows (Figure 11). The

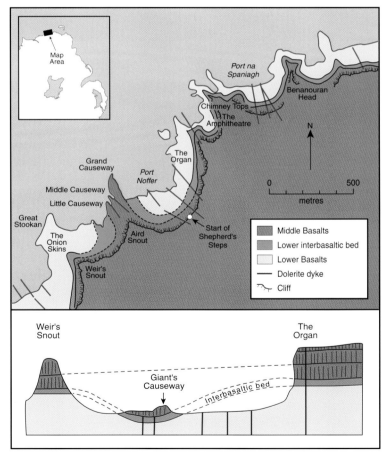

Figure 11: The Causeway Coast: *location and geology.*
After: Wilson and Manning, 1978.

Photo 13: Spheroidally weathered basalt corestones at 'the onion skins'.

interbasaltic bed formed as a deep, iron- and aluminium-rich tropical soil. It can be conveniently viewed in two locations. The first is approximately 100m below the Visitors' Centre along the road down to the Causeway. This exposure regularly sheds loose debris onto the road and occasionally large masses of fallen rock can be seen, which graphically illustrate the structural weakness of this bed when compared to the basalts. The second outcrop, below Roveran Valley Head (Figure 12), more closely resembles the original soil profile with the 'ghosts' of basalt blocks and the preserved intervening joint system. On top of the profile is an iron-rich layer similar to the lateritic layers that cap many soils in present-day savanna regions.

Below the interbasaltic bed the upper section of the Lower basalt also shows signs of weathering. The weathering here was not as intense as in the soil zone and consisted mainly of chemical alteration along joints to produce rounded **'corestones'** from joint-bounded basalt blocks (Photo 13). Such exfoliating 'corestones' can be seen at the aptly named 'onion skin rocks' above the sharp bend in the Causeway road by the Great Stookan headland (D 945443).

Above the interbasaltic bed are the thick lava flows of the Middle Basalts. These cooled slowly and formed dense networks of interlocked polygonal columns. It is assumed that the columns formed at right angles to the surface of the flow and so in most cases, such as The Organ, are near-vertical. However, in some areas the lavas flowed into valleys and inclined columns formed inwards from the valley sides. Where inclined columns are exposed in the cliffs they often form sites of active erosion such as the Amphitheatre and below Aird Snout above the Causeway. The most obvious of these infilled valleys is centred on the Causeway itself. Viewed from the sea the

Photo 14: Basalt columns of the Middle Causeway.

interbasaltic bed on either side of the Causeway dips and disappears below sea level bringing the columnar basalts down to the coast where they form the Grand, Middle and Little Causeways (Figure 11).

The Causeway Coast landscape

The columns of the Giant's Causeway form one of the most distinctive and widely recognised landforms in the British Isles and fully justify designation as a World Heritage Site, even though their physical extent is very limited (Photo 14). Ironically, however, because of the distinctive and intricate nature of their polygonal structure the rest of the site is often overlooked, even though the World Heritage designation includes the Tertiary volcanics and associated fossil soils as a whole. In particular, the designation draws attention to the structure of the Middle Basalt lava flows to the east of the Causeway, which were likened to architectural elements of a classical building by Tomkeieff (1940). Each lava sequence is seen to comprise a colonnade capped by an entablature (Photo 15). The colonnade describes a zone of regular vertical columns while the entablature comprises an upper, less regular zone. The Causeway itself is the colonnade of the first flow of the Causeway basalts and at The Organ this colonnade passes up into the entablature of the same flow. From a purely geomorphological standpoint it is the cliffs built from these flows that are of wider interest and demonstrate a tremendous variety of slope failures related to geological structure, marine erosion and human intervention.

Photo 15: Plaiskin Head: *the colonnade and entablature structures of the Middle Basalt can be seen above the red, lower interbasaltic bed.*

Slope form and instability

Cliff form is highly dependent upon the embayed shape of the coastline, which in turn depends on zones of relative resistance to erosion, related to the presence of doleritic dykes or structural variations in the basalt (Figure 11). Around the bays and headlands detailed profile form also depends on energy conditions at the foot of the cliff. In general terms, active basal erosion of bedrock produces vertical or near-vertical cliffs. Efficient removal of debris, but limited erosion of bedrock, allows slope form to adjust to the underlying geological structure and produces stepped cliffs. Impeded basal removal results in accumulation of screes that begin to mask the cliffs from which the debris derives. Ultimately, as a scree grows, its source area for new debris is diminished and it becomes less active. These combined effects have resulted in two broad slope classes.

Cliffs and slopes in bays

Within bays the slope foot zone comprises an extensive wave-cut platform mantled by large boulders which dissipate wave energy effectively. In places, groundwater in the form of springs and marshes flows on to the platform and this has created areas of considerable ecological interest. The presence of this platform has also allowed debris to accumulate from weathering of the cliffs and extensive scree slopes to form. Many scree slopes are now vegetated and may have formed during earlier, more active periods of weathering and cliff retreat since the last glaciation of the area (the Holocene period). The screes are mainly angular basalt debris (>50cm), but when stabilised this is covered by approximately 50cm of angular cobbles and gravel set in an organic rich, sandy clay matrix, strongly bound together by a dense root mat. Patches of bare scree are predominantly in the slope foot zone where wave attack might periodically over-steepen slopes.

Slope failures within the screes are often associated with poor drainage, and undercutting of slopes by the road and footpaths. These shallow failures are particularly common in Port Noffer, where a section of the lower footpath to the west of The Organ was completely destroyed in 1981. A similar failure below the Shepherd's Steps in 1994 also temporarily closed the path, but the ability of the landscape to absorb these failures is indicated by how difficult it is to identify the erosion scars left by these collapses. Although conditioned by undercutting and the natural failure plane between topsoil and scree, failures are triggered by periods of prolonged and/or intense rainfall. During these periods, surface horizons become saturated, cohesion of the topsoil is greatly reduced and a mud/debris flow can be triggered. As this flow moves downslope it loses water and transforms into a slide which ultimately mantles the lower slope in a debris cone or lobe. Subsequent runoff from the landslide scar washes this debris out on to the shore platform beyond the slope foot zone.

Above the screes are vertical or stepped cliffs which shed debris either as angular blocks or as toppled basalt columns. Both phenomena are induced by diurnal and seasonal moisture and temperature cycling, which exploits joint systems to weather the basalt through chemical alteration and mechanical processes such as **freeze/thaw**. Often, the fall of an individual block or column triggers the release of surrounding material and a considerable area of cliff may ultimately collapse. There is therefore a regular 'leakage' of debris from cliffs, interspersed with occasional larger falls. These falls either add an additional mantle to the screes or may temporarily reactivate the upper layer.

This overall pattern of erosion is widespread along the coast and at any one time it is possible to see a number of active and vegetated scars from falls and slides. These indicate long-term slope instability and suggest that these failures can occur without the necessity for human intervention.

Cliffs on headlands

Basal erosion and removal of cliff foot debris are more efficient and effective in these areas, in response to concentrated wave attack. Distinctions can, however, be made between the ends of headlands and their sides. Once initiated, headlands create **wave refraction** which concentrates wave energy along their flanks. The most active erosion and steepest cliffs are not at the ends of the headlands, therefore, but on their sides where they join the screes of

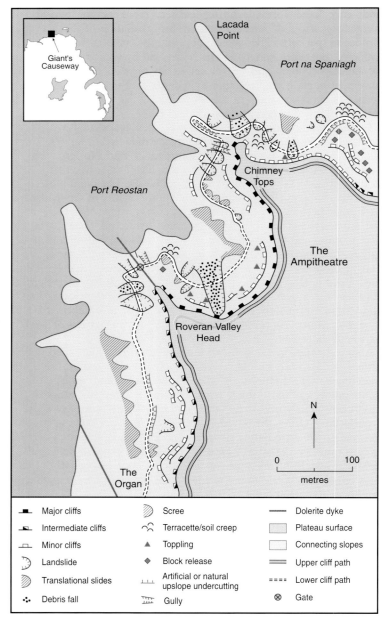

Figure 12: Geomorphology of the coast to the east of the Giant's Causeway,
*showing the concentration of rockfalls and landslides along the steeper slopes
of the headlands.*

intervening bays. The effect of concentrated basal erosion is to diminish geological control on slope form. In particular, the gentler slopes associated with the interbasaltic bed are steepened and in places disappear altogether to leave a vertical cliff.

All other factors being equal, major mass movements (collapses) are therefore, most likely to occur on the sides of headlands (Figure 12). This is particularly the case where the interbasaltic bed has been excavated to accommodate the cliff path, for example, below Roveran Valley Head. There is, however, evidence that this is a long-term pattern of erosion that is not dependent on human intervention. Along the coast it is possible to see natural arches, where basal erosion has cut through headlands, and numerous remnants of previous headlands in the form of sea **stacks**.

The effect of human intervention

Because of its international status, the Giant's Causeway attracts more than half a million visitors each year. Inevitably this places great pressure on the landscape, pressure that is accentuated by a raft of additional habitat directives (e.g. Area of Special Scientific Interest, National Nature Reserve) that help channel walkers along a limited number of routes. Even along the metalled road the natural instability of the site can be seen with the interbasaltic bed and 'onion-skin' rocks releasing a continuous supply of debris onto the surface. The most serious long-term threat occurs where the road cuts

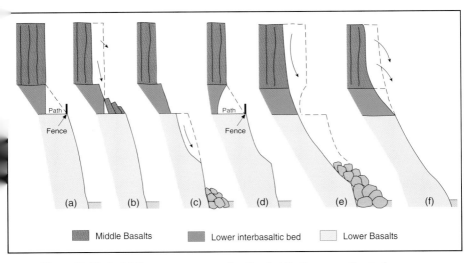

Figure 13: Typical failure sequences on a headland at the Causeway Coast where the lower footpath was cut into the interbasaltic bed: (a) initial excavation of interbasaltic bed to accommodate footpath, (b) toppling of undermined basalt columns, (c) slumping of Lower Basalts, (d) excavation of interbasaltic bed for reconstituted path, (e) major rotational failure of all three strata, and (f) gradual adjustment of slope to reflect underlying geological differences.

across a former mudslide (D 945441) approximately 120m below the Visitors' Centre. The continued movement of this slide can be seen in the cambering of the road and a series of tension cracks that must be regularly sealed to prevent water entering and possibly reactivating the slide. Along the foreshore in Port Ganny, on the approach to the Giant's Causeway the road is undermined by wave action while nearer the Giant's Causeway numerous angular dents in the road surface testify to the many block falls from Aird Snout.

These problems are significant because they impinge upon the busiest route, but the most dramatic effects of human intervention have occurred where the lower path has been cut into the cliff face, especially around headlands where slopes are steepest. Path construction necessitated excavation of the red interbasaltic bed and undermining of the overlying columnar basalts. Once this was done, it was inevitable that slope failures would eventually be triggered by periods of prolonged and/or intense rainfall that both reduce cohesion in the interbasaltic bed and reduce friction along joints within the basalt. A possible sequence for these failures is shown in Figure 13 and is typical of the major failure that initially closed the lower path in 1994 when a complete section of the cliff collapsed (Photo 16). A common precursor to these falls is the toppling of individual columns (Photo 17) and/or the steady fall of loose basalt debris onto the path. Although individual falls may have a limited lateral extent, it is their concentration along the steepest sections of cliff that has made their remediation impossible and that ultimately required the closure of the path to the general public.

The impact of path construction is not restricted to the headlands; many failures within the bays are associated with undercutting of scree slopes. Most commonly this produces small arcuate scars several metres in diameter which are caused by topsoil collapsing onto the path (Figure 14a). In zones of groundwater seepage, larger shallow flow/slides can strip both topsoil and the upper layer of scree (Figure 14b). Much larger falls, such as that seen in The Amphitheatre, can result in reactivation of screes and serious undermining of the cliff leading to rockfalls and cliff retreat (Figure 14c and Photo 18). Fortunately, the largest falls are relatively rare events but the smaller failures are a regular feature within the bays and require continual path maintenance and sometimes reconstruction.

Beyond the Causeway

The geomorphological interest of the north coast of Northern Ireland by no means ends at the Giant's Causeway. Westwards, and within sight of the Causeway, the stony foreshore of Portballintrae (D 9242-D 9243) is an eloquent testimony to how construction along the shoreline can alter wave energy patterns and rapidly strip sand from a beach. From Dunluce Castle (D 9041) it is possible to see again the contact between chalk and basalt and the tilted offshore islands of The Skerries formed by yet another dolerite sill.

Photo 16: A major rockfall below Lacada Point that closed the lower footpath in 1994. The fractured basalts above the interbasaltic bed have continued to shed debris ever since.

Photo 17: Toppling failure of Middle Basalt column where it was undermined by the lower coastal path.

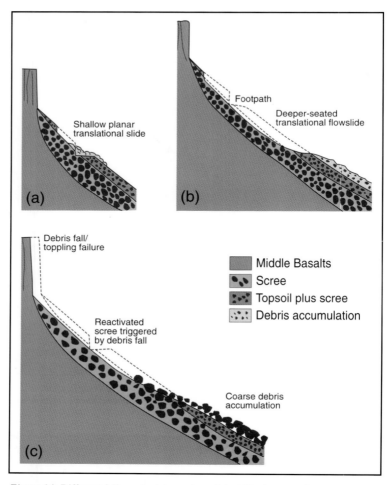

Figure 14: Different failures *(not drawn to scale) within the scree slopes:*
(a) small translational failure of topsoil layer where it has been undermined by the
path, (b) flowslide which strips the topsoil and upper layer of scree (this can destroy
the coastal path, as has happened below the Shepherd's Path, for example), and
(c) reactivation of screes associated with collapse and retreat of basalt cliff
(e.g. in The Amphitheatre, see Photo 18).

West of Portstewart, the course of the River Bann is deflected to the
west by Portstewart Strand and its extensive dune complex and enters
the sea nearer to Castlerock. Further west, at Downhill, the cliffs are
topped by the eighteenth century Mussenden Temple (D 759363),
which was built by the Fourth Earl of Bristol. In the late 1990s there
was much debate as to whether the Temple should be moved inland
from its cliff edge location or whether the cliff should be stabilised. It
was decided to pursue an engineering solution and the basalt blocks
below the Temple were 'bolted' in place.

Photo 18: Reactivated scree in The Amphitheatre and marked interbasaltic bed
below Lacada Point. It was a series of failures at this 'pinch point' along the
lower footpath that destroyed a section of the path in 1994 and led to its closure.
The debris from these falls can still be seen covering the grassy slope below the
interbasaltic bed.

   The potential for collapse of the basalts is illustrated to the west of
Downhill in the imposing cliffs of Binevenagh (D 6830-D 6931). This
marks the north-west corner of the plateau basalts and the rotational
failures below the inland cliffs are the equal of those on the east
Antrim coast. Each of these sites is worthy of explanation in their own
right, but that, as they say, is a story for another time.

GLOSSARY

Basalt. A fine-grained, dark-coloured sometimes glassy basic igneous rock formed as lava flows.

Corestone. A residual block of hard, unweathered rock surrounded by weathered material. Normally rounded, corestones may have begun as angular joint-bounded blocks.

Creep. Imperceptible, but continuous, movement of the upper layers (in this case, of till) of a slope down hill. Possibly related to repeated expansion and contraction associated with, for example, wetting and drying.

Dolerite. A medium-grained, dark-coloured, basic igneous rock. Composition is similar to basalt, but slower cooling beneath the Earth's surface produces larger crystals.

Dyke. A vertical or near-vertical intrusion of igneous rock – often doleritic.

Flashy river. One in which discharge rises rapidly after rainfall commences and falls almost as rapidly after it ceases. Often characterised by low flow conditions between storms.

Freeze/thaw. Repeated freezing and thawing of trapped water causing rock shattering and the widening of joints.

Glacial striae. Scratches on ice worn rocks caused by the forward movement of ice which is carrying rock fragments frozen into its base.

Isostasy. The process of maintaining the equilibrium of the Earth's crust, which in north-eastern Ireland has been affected by the weight of glacial ice, initially causing depression of the crust, and subsequent rebound following deglaciation.

Karst. Terrain created by limestone solution, characterised by drainage which disappears underground via solution hollows and solution-widened joints. Karst surfaces often exhibit a range of micro-solutional pits and channels. In marine karst these features are modified by salt weathering.

Lignite. Low-grade coal; intermediate between peat and bituminous coal.

Marine bench. A platform close to sea level usually cut by a variety of marine processes. Sometimes termed a wave-cut platform.

Raised beach. Beach deposits found in a position above present-day sea level.

Roche moutonnée. A glacially moulded mass of rock with a smooth upstream side formed by abrasion, and a rough downstream side formed by ice plucking.

Rotational failure. Landslip where a mass of rock moves downhill on a concave (upward) slip-plane, leaving the mass with a back-slope facing uphill.

Salt weathering. Breakdown of rock caused by the repeated crystallisation and expansion of salts within pores and joints.

Scree. Accumulation of mainly angular material which lies at an angle of approximately 32-35°, supplied by rockfall from cliffs above them.

Sill. Flat-lying mass of igneous rock intruded into other rocks conformably with their bedding.

Solution hollow. See Karst.

Stack. A pillar of rock beyond the coast cut off from the main cliff by erosion. May once have been connected to the mainland by a rock arch.

Terra rossa. Thin red-coloured soil rich in iron oxides and typically developed on limestones in the Mediterranean region.

Till. A sediment deposited by glacial ice that contains a range of particle sizes (poorly sorted) and rock types from a range of areas (erratics).

Wave cut platform. See marine bench.

Wave refraction. The change in direction of wave crests as they approach the shore, due to the shallowing of the water. The effect is to concentrate wave energy around headlands and to dissipate wave energy within embayments.

BIBLIOGRAPHY

Betts, N.L. (1992) 'The north Antrim flood of 1990', *Irish Geography*, 25, 2, pp. 138-48.

Bowen, D.Q. (1978) *Quaternary Geology*. Oxford: Pergamon Press.

Carter, R.W.G. (1982) 'Sea-level changes in Northern Ireland', *Proceedings of the Geologists' Association*, 93, 1, pp. 7-23.

Carter, R.W.G. (1991) *Shifting Sands: A study of the coast of Northern Ireland from Magilligan to Larne*. Countryside and Wildlife Research Series No. 2. Belfast: HMSO.

Carter, R.W.G. and Kitcher, K.J. (1979) 'The geomorphology of offshore sand bars on the north coast of Ireland', *Proceedings of the Royal Irish Academy*, 79(B), pp. 43-61.

Davies, G.L. and Stephens, N. (1978) *'The Geomorphology of the British Isles: Ireland'*. London: Methuen.

Devoy, R.J.N. (1985) 'The problems of a late-Quaternary land bridge between Britain and Ireland', *Quaternary Science Review*, 4, pp. 43-58.

Lyle, P. (1996) *A Geological Excursion Guide to the Causeway Coast*. Environment and Heritage Service (Department of the Environment NI). Belfast: HMSO.

Mallory, J.P. and McNeill, T.E. (1991) *The Archaeology of Ulster, from Colonization to Plantation*. Belfast: Institute of Irish Studies, Queen's University.

McKeever, P.J. (1999) *A Story Through Time: The formation of the scenic landscapes of Ireland (North)*. Belfast: Geological Survey of Northern Ireland.

Mitchell, F. and Ryan, M. (1997) *Reading the Irish Landscape*. Dublin: Town House.

Prior, D.B., Stephens, N. and Douglas, G.R. (1971) 'Some examples of mudflow and rockfall activity in north-east Ireland' in Brunsden, D. (ed) *Slopes, Form and Process*. Institute of British Geographers, special publication No. 3, pp. 129-40.

Smith, B.J. and Ferris, C. (1997) 'Giant's Causeway: management of erosion', *Geography Review*, 11, pp. 30-7.

Smith, B.J. and McAlister, J.J. (1995) 'Mineralogy, chemistry and palaeoenvironmental significance of an Early Tertiary Terra Rossa from Northern Ireland: a preliminary review', *Geomorphology*, 12, pp. 63-73.

Stephens, N. and Glasscock, R.E. (1970) *Irish Geographical Studies*. Queen's University Belfast.

Tomkeieff, S.I. (1940) 'The basalt lavas of the Giant's Causeway district of Northern Ireland', *Bulletin Volcanologique*, Serie 2, 6, pp. 89-143.

Whittow, J. (1975) *Geology and Scenery in Ireland*. Harmondsworth: Penguin.

Wilson, H.E. and Robbie, J.A. (1966) *Geology of the Country Around Ballycastle*. Belfast: HMSO.

Wilson, H.E. and Manning, P.I. (1978) *Geology of the Causeway Coast, Volume 1. Memoirs of the Geological Survey of Northern Ireland*. Belfast: HMSO.